rayo

An Imprint of HarperCollinsPublishers

UNGENIO HUEVODURO DON CHUMA

These are Condorito's closest friends, and they would become the Three Musketeers if Condorito ask them to. Their loyalty might be tested, but through adventures and misadventures it never fails.

YES, SIR...I'VE ALREADY SOLD MY HOUSE, MY PIANO, MY CAR, RADIO AND MOST OF MY CLOTHES!

WHO GOES THERE?

A BURGLAR

DON CUASI DOÑA TREMEBUNDA

Pushing up the social ladder with their mustaches, Yayita's parents are against her courtship with "that useless birdbrain." They support Pepe Cortisona any chance they get.

Matias

CG

garganta de Lata

While they're both Condorito's friends, they are very different from each other. CG is a free spirit, while Garganta prefers a free drink.

WASHINGTON

CONDORITO

YAYITA

Condorito's girlfriend. She is attractive, curvaceous and modern. She loves Condorito, but she lets Pepe Cortisona court her.

The best-loved idol in the Spanish-speaking world, everyone enjoys his adventures and laughing with him. Poor yet resourceful, Condorito is always a step ahead and helping his friends. His imagination gets him into all sorts of situations and eras.

pepe cortisona

Handsome, vain and a dandy, he is Condorito's eternal rival because he woos Yayita. Condorito calls him "meathead".

coné yuyito

Mischievous, ingenious, and adorable. He is Condorito's nephew, and she is Yayita's niece.

HarperCollins books may be purchased for educational, business, or sales promotional use. For information, please write: Special Markets Department, HarperCollins Publishers, 10 East 53rd Street, New York, NY 10022.

Collaborators: José Luis Gaete, Jorge Durán, Jorge Domínguez, Claudia Adriazola, Sebastián Schmidt, Jennifer King, Juan Américo Pastenes and María José Barandiarán

FIRST EDITION
Printed on acid-free paper

Library of Congress Cataloging-in-Publication Data is available upon request.

ISBN 0-06-077602-1

05 06 07 08 09 RRD 10 9 8 7 6 5 4 3 2 1

www.condorito.com

20

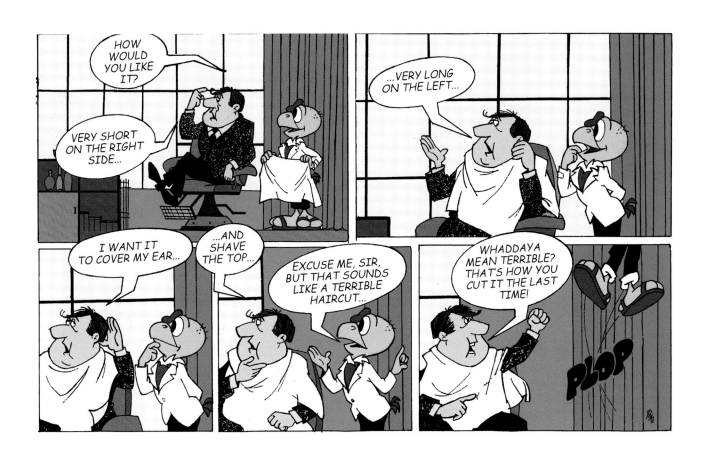

40

45

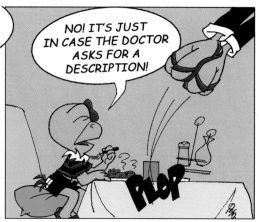

53

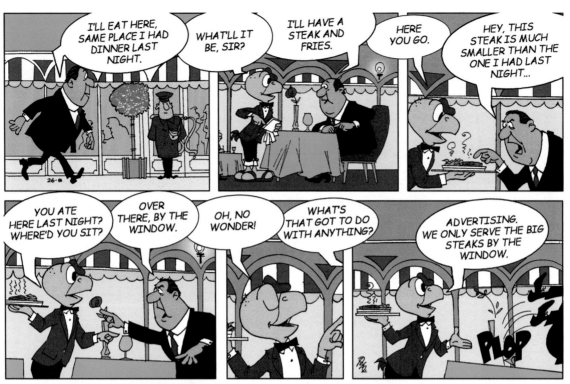

87

99

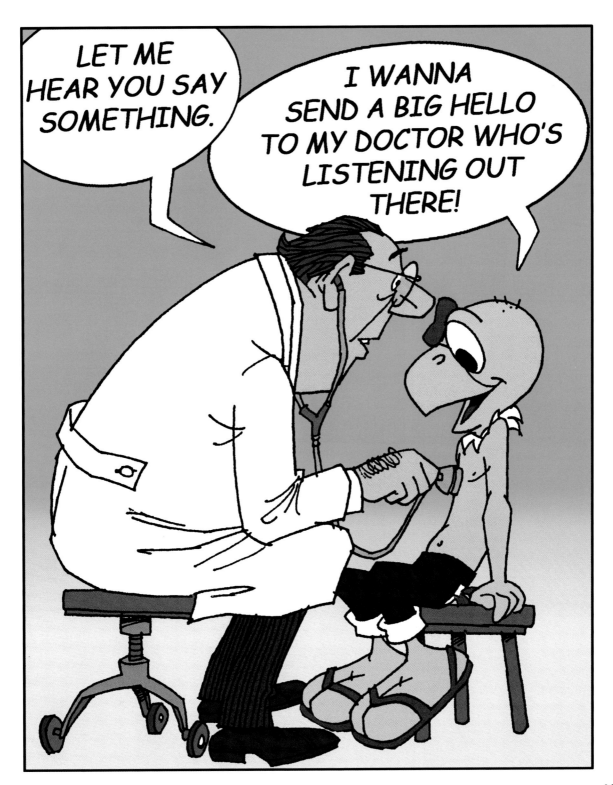

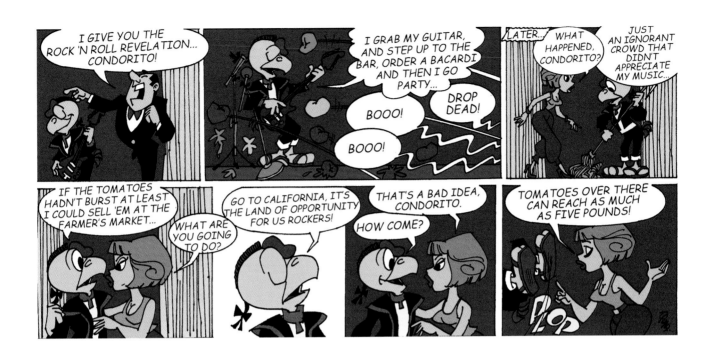

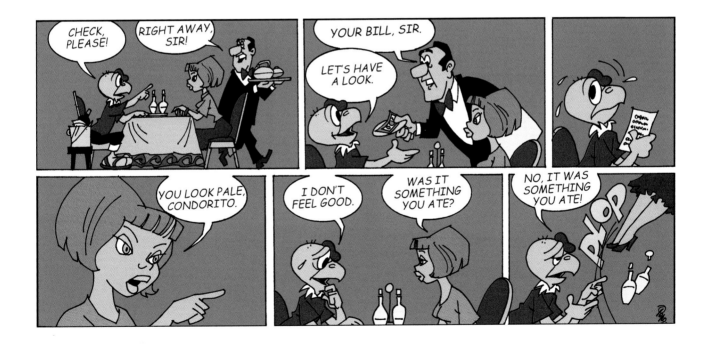